First hardcover edition, April 2020
Design by Mykel L. Brooks
Printed in the United States

ISBN: 978-1-7348285-0-4

Published in the United States by Evolving Still Publishing
a division of Evolving Still, LLC
Detroit, MI
www.evolvingstill.com

Evolving Still Publishing books are available at special discounts for bulk purchases for sales promotions or corporate use. Special editions, including personalized covers, excerpts of existing books, or books with corporate logos, can be created in large quantities for special needs. For more information, contact Evolving Still Publishing at contact@evolvingstill.com.

Table of Contents

Letter From the Author

First, I would like to thank each and every one of you for joining me on this journey of evolving. Striving to be an emotionally healthy person is not easy for most of us. In fact, it's one of the hardest things we've often done, so I am extremely thankful that you've trusted me along your journey. Writing this journal and establishing Evolving Still has helped me through so much and by creating this community, I am beyond grateful that I am able to use my passion to help not only myself but others.

The EDGE Journal was created as a tool to practice some of the most important aspects of emotional wellness. I created a guided journal because the most important step to Evolving is to be transparent with yourself. This journal contains four chapters that are filled with questions requiring you to dig deep and be your authentic self.

Chapter One: *Explore*, is intended for you to start relearning yourself. It is so easy to get caught up in the busyness of life that we forget the most important person, ourselves. Crazy enough, many of us live the majority of our lives not knowing who we are, so this chapter was designed for readers to not only get to know who they are but began to love that person as well.

Chapter *Two*: *Dream* is designed to explore your deepest desires, even the ones that are so big you wouldn't dare say them outloud. This chapter forces the question, in a perfect world, what are the things that you would want out of life.

Chapter Three: *Grow* was created to reveal the things you can work on to be the best version of yourself. Now that you are understanding who you are and the things you want, it's time to start making changes so that you can live your best life.

Last but not least, **Chapter Four:** *Equip* is meant to provide you with first steps to conquering your dreams. I know it may sound like a lot of promises in one book, but when you begin thinking and writing out the things you desire, you can begin to hold yourself accountable for the life that you want to live.

STILL *Evolving*

EBONI SAWYER

> "Knowing yourself is the beginning of all wisdom."
>
> *- Aristotle*

Explore

/ikˈsplôr/

Verb

To explore is to intentionally interact with
unfamiliar situations. To observe thoughts, ideas
and feelings for the purpose of self discovery.

list the things you **love** *about yourself.*

_____
_____
_____
_____
_____
_____
_____
_____
_____
_____
_____
_____
_____
_____
_____
_____

list the things you *need*
to **truly be happy.**

_____

_____

_____

_____

_____

_____

_____

_____

_____

_____

_____

_____

_____

_____

_____

_____

list the ways you
make yourself happy.

_____

_____

_____

_____

_____

_____

_____

_____

_____

_____

_____

_____

_____

_____

_____

_____

list the ways in which **others**
make you happy.

_____

_____

_____

_____

_____

_____

_____

_____

_____

_____

_____

_____

_____

_____

_____

list your favorite *self* care activities.

when is the **last** time you've done these things?

_____

_____

_____

_____

_____

_____

_____

_____

_____

_____

_____

_____

_____

_____

_____

"Let go of who you think you're supposed to be, embrace who you are."

– *Brene Brown*

write out a playlist that
describes *your life* right now.

_____

_____

_____

_____

_____

_____

_____

_____

_____

_____

_____

_____

_____

_____

what are your all time **favorite** movies?

what do you *love* about them?

_____

_____

_____

_____

_____

_____

_____

_____

_____

_____

_____

_____

_____

_____

_____

_____

_____

what are your *favorite things* to do?
what do these things say about you?

_____

_____

_____

_____

_____

_____

_____

_____

_____

_____

_____

_____

_____

_____

_____

_____

_____

how is **most of your time** spent?

what are some things you've
worked hard to achieve?

_____
_____
_____
_____
_____
_____
_____
_____
_____
_____
_____
_____
_____

"Once you really know yourself, can't nobody tell you nothing about you."

- Megan Thee Stallion

what are your favorite "titles" ?
what do these titles say about you?
who are you without these "titles"?

_____

_____

_____

_____

_____

_____

_____

_____

_____

_____

_____

_____

_____

who are your *role models*?
what about them do you admire?

_____

_____

_____

_____

_____

_____

_____

_____

_____

_____

_____

_____

_____

_____

_____

_____

how do you deal with *disappointment from others?*
from yourself?

_____

_____

_____

_____

_____

_____

_____

_____

_____

_____

_____

_____

_____

_____

_____

_____

what are you **prioritizing** in
your *life* right now?
why is this important to you?

_____

_____

_____

_____

_____

_____

_____

_____

_____

_____

_____

_____

_____

_____

_____

what are some things
going really well in your life right now?

_____

_____

_____

_____

_____

_____

_____

_____

_____

_____

_____

_____

_____

_____

"Be you, love you. Always, all ways."

– Alex Elle

list **and** explain some things
you are *looking forward to.*

_____

_____

_____

_____

_____

_____

_____

_____

_____

_____

_____

_____

_____

_____

_____

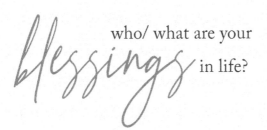

who/ what are your *blessings* in life?

_____

_____

_____

_____

_____

_____

_____

_____

_____

_____

_____

_____

_____

_____

_____

_____

_____

_____

list the things you are *passionate* about.
what **drives** these passions?

_____

_____

_____

_____

_____

_____

_____

_____

_____

_____

_____

_____

_____

_____

_____

describe your *purpose.*

what is your "*why*"?

***if your purpose has not found you yet, I encourage you to
bookmark this page and come back to it as you continue on your
journey of evolving.**

_____

_____

_____

_____

_____

_____

_____

_____

_____

_____

_____

_____

_____

_____

_____

_____

_____

write a letter to yourself.

explain what *evolving* means to you.

_____

_____

_____

_____

_____

_____

_____

_____

_____

_____

_____

_____

_____

_____

_____

_____

_____

_____

"If your dreams don't scare you, they aren't big enough."

– T.D. Jakes

Dream

/dreem/
Verb

To dream is to consider as a possibility.
To imagine or picture that something
desirable can manifest.

describe your *dream life*.
what makes this life ideal?

_____

_____

_____

_____

_____

_____

_____

_____

_____

_____

_____

_____

_____

_____

_____

_____

if there is any situation that you could redo, what
would it be and **what would you do differently?**

_____

_____

_____

_____

_____

_____

_____

_____

_____

_____

_____

_____

_____

_____

what's one thing from your **childhood**
that you wish could have been *different?*

_____

_____

_____

_____

_____

_____

_____

_____

_____

_____

_____

_____

_____

_____

_____

_____

what's one thing or *experience* you wish to
pass on to your child/children?

_____

_____

_____

_____

_____

_____

_____

_____

_____

_____

_____

_____

_____

_____

_____

_____

what's one thing or experience you
want your child/children to do **differently**?

"You have brains in your head.
You have feet in your shoes.
You can steer yourself
in any direction you choose."

– Dr. Seuss

what is a conversation that you have
always wished to have?

with *whom* would it be?

_____

_____

_____

_____

_____

_____

_____

_____

_____

_____

_____

_____

_____

_____

if you could have an *unlimited supply* of
something from anywhere or any place
for the rest of your life,
what would it be?

_____

_____

_____

_____

_____

_____

_____

_____

_____

_____

_____

_____

_____

_____

_____

describe your *perfect* holiday.

_____

_____

_____

_____

_____

_____

_____

_____

_____

_____

_____

_____

_____

_____

_____

_____

if you could **give** your loved one any gift
without price being a concern,
what would it be
and *who would you give it to?*

---

if you could **receive** any gift
without price being a concern,
what would it be?

_____

_____

_____

_____

_____

_____

_____

_____

_____

_____

_____

_____

_____

_____

_____

"Never be limited by other people's
limited imagination."

- Dr. Mae Jemison

describe your *dream* career.

_____

_____

_____

_____

_____

_____

_____

_____

_____

_____

_____

_____

_____

_____

_____

_____

if you **never had to work again,**
what would you do with your life?

_____

_____

_____

_____

_____

_____

_____

_____

_____

_____

_____

_____

_____

_____

_____

if you could live anywhere in the world,
where would you live?
why?

_____

_____

_____

_____

_____

_____

_____

_____

_____

_____

_____

_____

_____

_____

_____

_____

_____

describe your *dream* home.

_____

_____

_____

_____

_____

_____

_____

_____

_____

_____

_____

_____

_____

_____

_____

_____

_____

_____

_____

if you were asked to do a TED Talk
what would you talk about?

_____

_____

_____

_____

_____

_____

_____

_____

_____

_____

_____

_____

_____

_____

_____

_____

_____

_____

"If you want to have a life that is worth living, a life that expresses your deepest feelings and emotions and cares and dreams, you have to fight for it."

- Alice Walker

what is your *dream* vacation?
are you traveling alone or with others?

_____
_____
_____
_____
_____
_____
_____
_____
_____
_____
_____
_____
_____
_____
_____
_____

if you were given a million dollars
what's the *first thing* you would do?

_____

_____

_____

_____

_____

_____

_____

_____

_____

_____

_____

_____

_____

_____

explain what needs to happen for you to be able to describe your life as a success.

_____

_____

_____

_____

_____

_____

_____

_____

_____

_____

_____

_____

_____

_____

_____

if you could choose any problem in the
world to *fix*, what would it be and why?

_____

_____

_____

_____

_____

_____

_____

_____

_____

_____

_____

_____

_____

_____

_____

write a letter to the *best* version of yourself. what have you accomplished?

"I have discovered in life that there are ways
of getting almost anywhere you want to go,
if you really want to go."

– *Langston Hughes*

Grow

/groh/

Verb

To grow is to progressively develop. To create or
produce results especially by deliberate
effort over time.

what can you do for yourself to be
a **happier** individual?

_____

_____

_____

_____

_____

_____

_____

_____

_____

_____

_____

_____

_____

_____

_____

_____

_____

what can you do to be a *better*
friend, child, parent, and/or partner?

_____

_____

_____

_____

_____

_____

_____

_____

_____

_____

_____

_____

_____

_____

_____

_____

_____

_____

what can you do to be a *better* student, teacher, and/or mentor?

_____

_____

_____

_____

_____

_____

_____

_____

_____

_____

_____

_____

_____

_____

what are some things you've
limited yourself from *accomplishing*?
why have you done this?

_____

_____

_____

_____

_____

_____

_____

_____

_____

_____

_____

_____

_____

_____

how would you like *others* to describe you?
what do the qualities you've listed
say about the person that you are?

_____

_____

_____

_____

_____

_____

_____

_____

_____

_____

_____

_____

_____

_____

_____

"The way must be in you; the destination also must be in you and not somewhere else in space or time. If that kind of self-transformation is being realized in you, you will arrive."

–Nhat Hanh

what's a skill that you want to *learn*?
why haven't you learned it yet?

---

list all of your strengths.
in what ways can you
improve/use them to your advantage?

_____

_____

_____

_____

_____

_____

_____

_____

_____

_____

_____

_____

_____

_____

_____

_____

list all of your weaknesses.
in what ways can you
make them a part of your strengths?

_____

_____

_____

_____

_____

_____

_____

_____

_____

_____

_____

_____

_____

_____

what, if any, are some of your *health* goals?

_____

_____

_____

_____

_____

_____

_____

_____

_____

_____

_____

_____

_____

_____

_____

_____

what, if any, are some of your
mental health goals?

_____

_____

_____

_____

_____

_____

_____

_____

_____

_____

_____

_____

_____

_____

_____

_____

"The only thing that's keeping you from getting what you want is the story you keep telling yourself."

– *Tony Robbins*

what's the **best** advice you've ever received?
how did this advice *shape* your life?

_____

_____

_____

_____

_____

_____

_____

_____

_____

_____

_____

_____

_____

_____

_____

_____

choose a *difficult* situation that you're experiencing. what advice would you give someone in that same situation?

_____
_____
_____
_____
_____
_____
_____
_____
_____
_____
_____
_____
_____
_____
_____
_____
_____
_____

what **relationship** in your life can you *mend?*
what's stopped you from doing it?

_____
_____
_____
_____
_____
_____
_____
_____
_____
_____
_____
_____
_____
_____
_____

is there anyone that you wish would forgive you?
what caused you to do what you did that
strained the relationship?

_____

_____

_____

_____

_____

_____

_____

_____

_____

_____

_____

_____

_____

_____

_____

_____

who are the *people* in your life that
inspire you to be a better person?
what about them speaks to who you
want to be?

_____

_____

_____

_____

_____

_____

_____

_____

_____

_____

_____

_____

_____

_____

_____

_____

"I have learned over the years that when one's mind is made up, this diminishes fear."

- Rosa Parks

who are some people you need to
let go in order to become your **best** self?

_____

_____

_____

_____

_____

_____

_____

_____

_____

_____

_____

_____

_____

_____

_____

_____

what are some things you need to **let go** in
order to become your best self?

_____

_____

_____

_____

_____

_____

_____

_____

_____

_____

_____

_____

_____

_____

_____

explain a situation that you possibly regret but if
given the chance **wouldn't do** differently.
write out why you *stand by* the ultimate results.

---

what's the *one* thing that is keeping
you from **evolving** in life?

_____

_____

_____

_____

_____

_____

_____

_____

_____

_____

_____

_____

_____

_____

_____

write a letter to yourself, explaining why it is
imperative that you continue to *grow,* no matter
what phase of life you are in.

_____
_____
_____
_____
_____
_____
_____
_____
_____
_____
_____
_____
_____
_____
_____
_____

"In order to evolve, you must be willing to do the work required."

-Eboni Sawyer

Equip

\ i-'kwip

Verb

To equip is to prepare for action by appropriate provisioning. To make ready beforehand for some purpose, use, or activity.

list some things that you could do to **improve**
your *emotional health*?

_____

_____

_____

_____

_____

_____

_____

_____

_____

_____

_____

_____

_____

_____

_____

_____

write out a "stress plan" for things you can do
when life gets stressful.

_____

_____

_____

_____

_____

_____

_____

_____

_____

_____

_____

_____

_____

_____

_____

_____

what are some things you can do to quickly
improve your *mood*?

_____

_____

_____

_____

_____

_____

_____

_____

_____

_____

_____

_____

_____

_____

what are some things that will quickly lower your mood?
how can you **prevent** these things from
affecting you as much?

_____

_____

_____

_____

_____

_____

_____

_____

_____

_____

_____

_____

_____

_____

_____

_____

check your calendar for some time to plan a *"Me"* day.
write out the date and time in this book to hold yourself
accountable to taking that day off.

_____

_____

_____

_____

_____

_____

_____

_____

_____

_____

_____

_____

_____

_____

"For life to work for you, you must equip yourself with the power of change."

– *Sunday Adelaja*

write out some ideas on how you can begin re-learning
who you are. what does *learning yourself* look like?

_____

_____

_____

_____

_____

_____

_____

_____

_____

_____

_____

_____

_____

_____

_____

describe how you *plan* to increase your knowledge? what are some **new** things you can learn and how do you go about learning them?

_____

_____

_____

_____

_____

_____

_____

_____

_____

_____

_____

_____

_____

_____

_____

list five books you want to read *this year*.
why did you choose these books?

_____
_____
_____
_____
_____
_____
_____
_____
_____
_____
_____
_____
_____
_____
_____

what are **five** things you can do to improve your health? describe in detail how you can *achieve* these things.

_____

_____

_____

_____

_____

_____

_____

_____

_____

_____

_____

_____

_____

_____

_____

_____

"**Nothing will work unless you do.**"

- Maya Angelou

how can you incorporate *healthy* eating into your daily life?

_____

_____

_____

_____

_____

_____

_____

_____

_____

_____

_____

_____

_____

_____

_____

_____

_____

what can *you* do to make your day to day life **easier**?

_____

_____

_____

_____

_____

_____

_____

_____

_____

_____

_____

_____

_____

_____

make a list of **goals** for the next month.
try out the "STILL" method to actually plan
these goals out.

_____

_____

_____

_____

_____

_____

_____

_____

_____

_____

_____

_____

_____

_____

what are some simple steps you can take to make
your "*dreams*" become your reality?

_____

_____

_____

_____

_____

_____

_____

_____

_____

_____

_____

_____

_____

_____

_____

focus on the first step you need to follow your dreams. what can you do in the **next month** to start theprocess of completing this step?

_____

_____

_____

_____

_____

_____

_____

_____

_____

_____

_____

_____

_____

_____

_____

_____

"All excuses are corrupt."

- Bishop Charles H. Ellis III

how can you hold yourself **accountable**?

_____

_____

_____

_____

_____

_____

_____

_____

_____

_____

_____

_____

_____

_____

_____

who are the people you can *count on* to
hold you accountable?

---

write a letter to someone that **hurt you.**

_____

_____

_____

_____

_____

_____

_____

_____

_____

_____

_____

_____

_____

write a letter to someone that **you hurt**.

_____

_____

_____

_____

_____

_____

_____

_____

_____

_____

_____

_____

_____

_____

_____

_____

what can you do in the next thirty days to
evolve and show up as your best self?

_____

_____

_____

_____

_____

_____

_____

_____

_____

_____

_____

_____

_____

_____

_____

_____

write a thank you letter to the person that you
are. without them you wouldn't be here on
your journey of

evolving.

_____

_____

_____

_____

_____

_____

_____

_____

_____

_____

_____

_____

_____

_____

_____